Wipe-clean
Investigating
Living Things

Illustrated by Elisa Paganelli

Written by Hannah Watson
Designed by Stephanie Jeffries

Expert advice from Dr. John Rostron
and Dr. Margaret Rostron

Hop

Open out the fold-out page at the back. It has labelled pictures to help you answer the questions.

Gloria

Wolfy

There are answers, helpful diagrams and notes for grown-ups at the back of the book.

Series Editor: Felicity Brooks

Parts of a plant

Gloria and Pin have drawn pictures of some flowers they like.
Label each drawing with the names of the plant parts using these words:

leaf   flower   stem

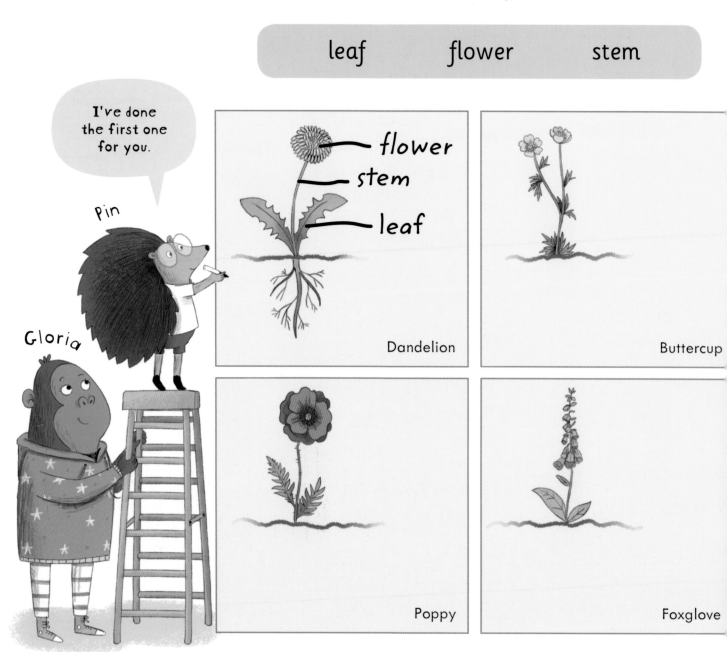

I've done the first one for you.

Pin

Gloria

flower
stem
leaf

Dandelion

Buttercup

Poppy

Foxglove

Gloria and Pin forgot to draw the roots of three of the plants.
Use your pen to add the roots, then label them.

Don't forget...

Don't forget to draw little root hairs. These take up water and substances called nutrients from the soil. You can see some root hairs on the opposite page and fold-out page.

The four main parts of a plant each have a job to do to help the plant live and grow. Trace over the dotted lines from each label to a plant part to show what it does.

Pollen is a yellow powder found inside flowers. Ovules are the eggs of plants.

Contains the pollen and ovules for making seeds

Carries water to the rest of the plant and supports it

Use light to make food for the plant

Draw up water and nutrients from the soil, and anchor the plant

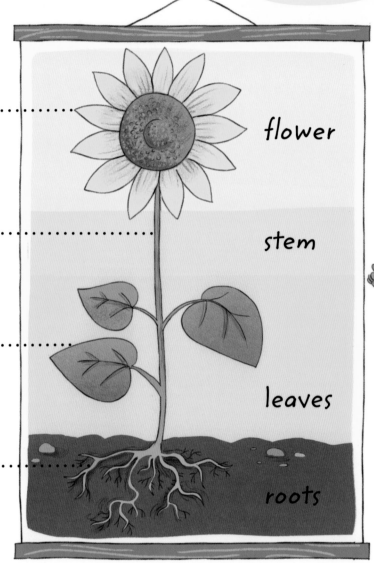

flower

stem

leaves

roots

A tree's trunk does the same job as a plant's stem.

Kat

Read these sentences and put a tick next to three facts that you think are true. Put a cross next to one that's false.

☐ Plant stems hold plants up towards the light.

☐ Root hairs on the root help the plant to take in sunlight.

☐ A flower's bright petals and sweet scent attract insects.

☐ Leaves are vital in helping the plant make its food.

Life and growth

Ping and Hop want to plant some flowers. They've made a list of things they think all plants need to grow. Draw a star next to each thing that plants really need.

Nutrients are the parts of the soil that help plants grow.

Hop

Ping and Hop's list

a sunhat

air

water

enough room to grow

nutrients from the soil

light

beautiful music

plant pots with flowers on them

a rainbow

The animals have had some ideas for things they could do to help their flowers grow.

Wear green gardening gloves.

Water the flowers.

Label the flowers.

Draw a star next to the three you think will help, please.

Ping

Add nutrients to the soil.

Carry things in a wheelbarrow.

Mark out enough room.

Bruce wants to plant a tree next to the flowers. He's talking with Kat about the things his tree needs to grow. Circle each idea you think is correct.

A tree won't need nutrients.

Both trees and flowers need air.

My tree will need more room than a flower.

I think flowers need more water than trees.

Bruce

Kat

Look at the other plants Bruce wants to put with the flowers. Draw a line to link each plant with the best idea for where it should grow.

cactus

water lily

moss

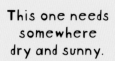

Hop

This plant grows best in a damp, shady place.

Kat

This one needs somewhere dry and sunny.

Ping

This grows best in a watery place, such as a pond.

Try at home...

Ask your grown-up if you can look after a plant at home. What things would you need for it to grow?

More about life and growth

Wolfy's leaving his plants at home while he's on holiday for a week.

Before Wolfy's holiday:

When he gets back he notices his plants aren't growing very well.

After Wolfy's holiday:

Look carefully at Wolfy's healthy plants before his holiday, and then when he's back. Write how plant 1 has changed on the lines below.

Wipe the lines clean.

Choose another plant, and write how it has changed. Keep going until you have written about each plant.

Wolfy has realized that each plant was missing something it needed. Look at his gardening book to help him work out what each one was missing.

What's wrong with my plant?

Answer the questions and follow the lines to find out why your plant isn't growing well. Then, see what to do to solve the problem.

Looking after your plants
Vol. 1

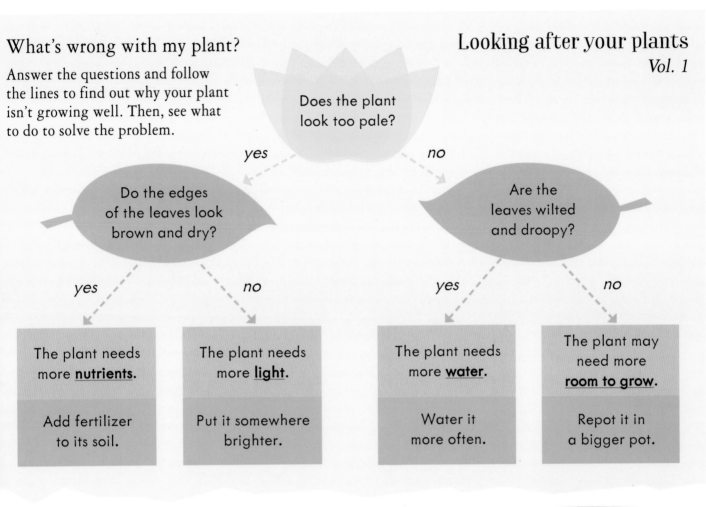

Does the plant look too pale?

yes   *no*

Do the edges of the leaves look brown and dry?

Are the leaves wilted and droopy?

yes   *no*   *yes*   *no*

The plant needs more **nutrients**.	The plant needs more **light**.	The plant needs more **water**.	The plant may need more **room to grow**.
Add fertilizer to its soil.	Put it somewhere brighter.	Water it more often.	Repot it in a bigger pot.

Using the gardening book, work out what plant 1 needs. Then, write '1' in the correct box below. Do the same for plants 2, 3 and 4.

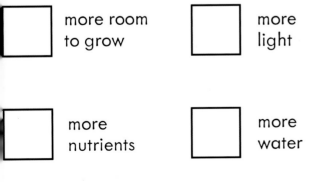

☐ more room to grow   ☐ more light

☐ more nutrients   ☐ more water

My sunflower's so tall now. I think the old pot was too small for its roots.

Water and plants

Ideas about what may happen in an experiment are called <u>predictions</u>.
Things you see happening in an experiment are called <u>observations</u>.
Things you learn from an experiment are called <u>conclusions</u>.

The animals are doing an experiment to see how flowers use water.
They've put a white flower into a jar of water with red food colouring in it.

<u>Day 1</u>

First, write a <u>prediction</u> of the experiment in the space below.

The flower will...

<u>Day 2</u>

Now, write an <u>observation</u>.

The flower has...

The animals are working out the <u>conclusions</u> from their experiment. Circle the conclusions you think are correct.

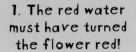

1. The red water must have turned the flower red!

2. The experiment shows that water goes through the stem to other parts of the plant.

3. The flower will turn red every time, whatever the colour of the water.

4. The petals of the flower must need water too.

5. If we left the plant in yellow sand, it would turn yellow.

6. It's only white flowers that need water to go through their stems to the rest of the plant.

Wipe the opposite page clean.

Gloria and Zeb do the experiment again with a new flower and <u>blue</u> water. Write a <u>prediction</u> of what you think will happen in the space on the opposite page.

Read these sentences about how plants use water. Put ticks next to two that are true, and crosses next to two that are false.

☐ Stems carry water up from the roots and take it to the rest of the plant.

☐ The flowers of a plant need water.

☐ Plants create their own water.

☐ Plants lose water through their roots.

Pollination

Pollination happens when a bee, another insect or the wind carries pollen (the yellow powder inside flowers) from one flower to another. When a flower has been pollinated, it can make seeds.

Look at the pictures below to see how pollination works. Trace the numbers and add a label to each picture using these words:

hive   pollen   bee   nectar

A bee flies over some flowers, attracted by their bright colours and sweet scent. It's looking for a sweet liquid called nectar.

The bee collects some nectar, which it will use to make honey. As it does this, some pollen sticks to its furry body.

When the bee visits another flower, some pollen may be brushed off. This flower is now pollinated, and may make seeds.

The bee visits lots of flowers, sipping their nectar and spreading their pollen before it flies back to its home, called a hive.

Pin has made a list of words to do with pollination. Help her match the words to their meanings by drawing lines between them.

pollen	a yellow powder found in flowers
seed	a sweet liquid found in flowers that bees use to make honey
nectar	when pollen is carried from one flower to another
pollination	a small object that plants make that can become a new plant

Put ticks next to two sentences that are true, and crosses next to two that are false. You can use the information on the opposite page to help you.

☐ a) Bees collect pollen to make honey.

☐ b) Bright colours and sweet scents attract bees to flowers.

☐ c) Some pollen is carried from flower to flower by the wind.

☐ d) Pollination is when nectar is carried from plant to plant.

How flowers make seeds

When a flower has been pollinated, a process called <u>fertilization</u> can happen. Flowers that have been fertilized can make seeds. Here's how:

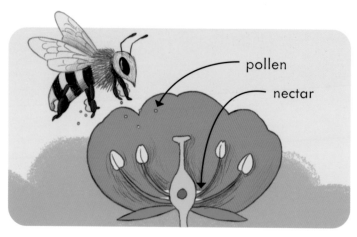

1. A bee arrives at a flower to collect nectar. If it's carrying pollen from another flower, this may be brushed off.

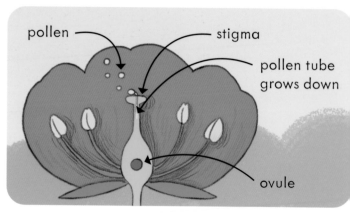

2. If a grain of pollen sticks to a part of the flower called a stigma, it forms a pollen tube which grows down to a part called the ovule.

3. When the pollen tube joins the ovule, the ovule has been fertilized and can start to develop into a seed.

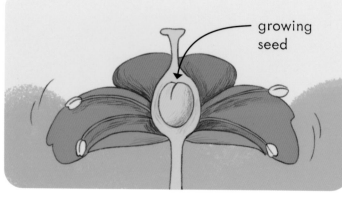

4. The flower starts to fade and the petals fall off. The fertilized ovule develops into a seed inside a seedhead, pod, fruit or nut.

Draw a line from each word below to its meaning.

ovule	the part of a flower that develops into a seed
pollen	when pollen from one flower joins the ovule of another to make a seed
fertilization	a yellow powder found inside flowers

Pin's a bit muddled about how fertilization works. Look at the pictures on the opposite page and write an explanation for her.

Help me understand how flowers make seeds, please.

First, a bee...

Then, the pollen...

A pollen tube...

A fertilized ovule...

Once seeds have been made, they need to move away from their parent plant. This is known as seed <u>dispersal</u>. Seeds have all kinds of ways of moving about.

Look! These seeds are floating on the breeze.

Some seeds are dispersed (spread) by the wind. They are often feathery or wing-shaped.

Some seeds have tiny hooks that stick to an animal's fur. They drop off in another place when the animal scratches or cleans itself.

There's a seed stuck to my fur.

When an animal eats fruit, berries or nuts, it swallows the seeds inside them. These are dispersed when the animal poos them out.

Some seeds are spread by explosion. A seed pod bursts open and the seeds shoot out.

Turn the page to help the animals learn more about dispersal.

Seed dispersal

The animals collected the seeds below to investigate different kinds of seed dispersal. The labels say where each seed was found.

sycamore seed

wood avens seedhead

dandelion seed

pea

Found by Wolfy — <u>spinning in the wind to the ground</u>

Found by Gloria — stuck to her fur

Found by Pin — blown through the air by the wind

Found by Ping — exploding from its pea pod

burdock burr

apple seed

cherry stone

scotch broom seeds

Found by Kat — "This one stuck to me as I went past."

Found by Pat — beside an apple half-eaten by an animal

Found by Hop — beside a cherry half-eaten by an animal

Found by Zeb — near a pod that had exploded

Can you work out how each seed moved away from its parent plant? Underline the part of each label that might be a clue. The first one has been done for you.

Put a tick in the correct box to show whether each seed was dispersed by the <u>wind</u>, <u>explosion</u>, or by <u>animals</u>. Use the information you underlined to help you. Hop has done a couple already.

wind	✓		✓					
animal		✓			✓	✓	✓	
explosion				✓				✓

Hop has some ideas about why it's better for seeds <u>not</u> to grow next to the plant they came from. Draw a big cross over any ideas you think are incorrect.

?
?

The plant would feel jealous that the seed was growing so close to it.

The parent plant's roots would take up most of the water the seed needed to grow.

The plant would die if the seed landed next to it.

The plant wouldn't leave the seed enough room to grow.

The plant would block the light so not enough would reach the new plant.

Food and nutrition

Animals need to eat food to get energy and nutrients.
Nutrients are things all living things need to survive and grow.

A <u>carnivore</u> is an animal that gets energy and nutrients from meat (including insects and fish). A <u>herbivore</u> gets energy and nutrients from plants. An <u>omnivore</u> gets energy and nutrients from both meat and plants.

The animals are talking about the foods they eat.
Write **C**, **H** or **O** on each card to show whether each animal is a carnivore (**C**), herbivore (**H**) or omnivore (**O**).

Wolves eat meat – and lots of it!

Porcupines like lots of different plants.

Parrots eat seeds, nuts, flowers and fruit.

Zebras like grass best, but also eat herbs, twigs, leaves and bark.

Meerkats mostly eat insects, but we eat plants too.

Penguins love to eat fish.

For each animal, put one tally mark (|) in the correct row of this chart to record whether it is a carnivore, herbivore or omnivore. Fill in the totals. Then, draw a circle around the largest total.

			Total
carnivores			
herbivores			
omnivores			

At his restaurant, Bruce serves meals based on what each customer likes to eat. Help him decide which meal he should give each animal by writing 'bear', 'lion' or 'horse' on the labels under the meals.

Now write **C**, **H** or **O** on the labels to show whether the meal is best for a carnivore, a herbivore or an omnivore.

Update the chart at the top of the page by adding a mark for the lion, bear and horse in the correct rows.

Fill in the new totals. Then, draw a circle around the largest total.

Food groups

The foods that humans eat can be split into different groups. You can see a picture of them on the fold-out page. A healthy diet contains a balance of foods from all the groups.

Draw a line to link each food group below with one of the supermarket signs. This will help Gloria label the aisles of Parkview Supermarket.

I've done one for you. Carbohydrates are found in foods such as bread, cereal, potatoes and pasta.

Fruit and vegetables   Fats and sugars   Dairy   Protein   Carbohydrates

Ping has arrived with his shopping list. Next to each thing on his list, write the name of the aisle where he will find it.

My meals of fish have lots of protein in them.

milk

bananas

bread

fish

cookies

Can you finish labelling this pie chart's key with the food groups? Kat and Zeb's speech bubbles and the picture on the fold-out page will help you.

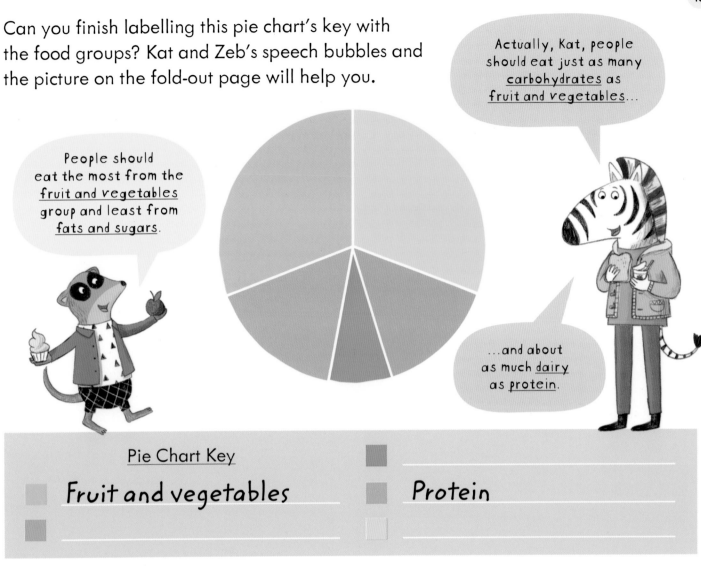

Actually, Kat, people should eat just as many <u>carbohydrates</u> as <u>fruit and vegetables</u>...

People should eat the most from the <u>fruit and vegetables</u> group and least from <u>fats and sugars</u>.

...and about as much <u>dairy</u> as <u>protein</u>.

<u>Pie Chart Key</u>

Fruit and vegetables

Protein

Kat wants to make a balanced meal for a human. She knows it needs foods from different groups, but she's not sure which of these two meals is best. Write the food groups each meal contains below. Draw a star next to the most balanced meal.

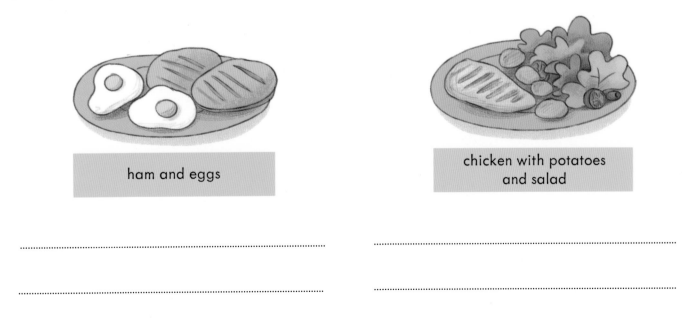

ham and eggs

chicken with potatoes and salad

All about skeletons

An <u>endoskeleton</u> is a skeleton <u>inside</u> the body.
Humans and the animals in this book have endoskeletons.
<u>Exoskeletons</u> are skeletons <u>outside</u> the body.
Lots of bugs and shellfish (such as crabs) have exoskeletons.

The animals are learning about x-rays, which are pictures (made by a machine) of the bones inside a body (a skeleton). You can see a picture of a human skeleton on the fold-out page.

> You can see flippers and feet just like mine.

> Look Ping, this one is a penguin's skeleton.

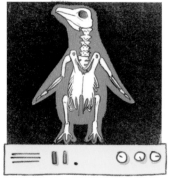

The animals have realized that although they are all different, they all have skeletons <u>inside</u> their bodies. These are known as <u>endoskeletons</u>.

> Most birds have very light skeletons so we can fly.

> My tail is part of my skeleton.

> What about this bug? Does it have a skeleton?

> My skeleton is very strong.

Kat looks at the bug with a magnifying glass. Its body has a hard outer coating, like a thin shell. This is a skeleton outside its body, called an <u>exoskeleton</u>.

exoskeleton

The map below shows some of the animals in the animal park.

- Take a guess at which animals have <u>endoskeletons</u>. Circle their names.
- Draw a line under all the animals that you think have <u>exoskeletons</u>.

You can check the answers at the back of the book. Then, wipe the page clean and have another go.

I know that most bugs have <u>exoskeletons</u>...

ANIMAL PARK EAST SITE

INSECT HOUSE

Parrots

Grasshoppers

Millipedes

Cockroaches

TROPICAL ZONE

Monkeys

Stick insects

Hippos

Crabs

Lions

Jellyfish

SAFARI ZONE

AQUARIUM

Giraffes

Octopus

Some animals, such as jellyfish, have no skeletons at all. They are known as <u>soft-bodied</u>.

- Put a dot next to the names of the animals that you think are <u>soft-bodied</u>.

Skeletons and muscles

Skeletons are important because they <u>protect</u> parts inside the body called organs. They also <u>support</u> the body and help it to stand up and <u>move</u> about.

An <u>organ</u> is a part of your body that does a special job, such as your heart or lungs.

Use the words in the panels below to label the picture, showing which part of the human skeleton <u>protects</u> which organ. Look at the skeleton picture on the fold-out page to help you.

parts of the skeleton

pelvis   skull   ribcage

organs inside body

heart   bladder   brain

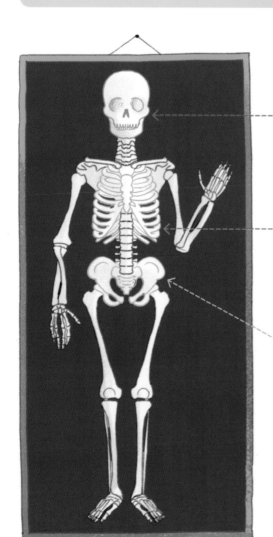

part of the skeleton		organ
SKULL	protects the	BRAIN
RIBCAGE	protects the	HEART
PELVIS	protects the	BLADDER

A helmet protects your skull when you are skateboarding.

Wipe away the label in the blue rectangle.

Can you think of another organ that the ribcage protects? Use the fold-out page to help you. Wipe the blue rectangle on the opposite page clean and write that organ in instead.

Read Kat's ideas about how skeletons help to support the body. Put ticks next to the two that are correct and crosses next to the two wrong ones.

☐ Skeletons help humans to stand upright.

☐ Skeletons make it harder to move.

☐ Skeletons are very strong.

☐ Skeletons don't protect the organs.

Skeletons also work with muscles to help the body move. Look at these diagrams, showing how muscles work.

Try this...

Pulling your arm up

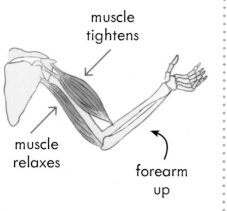

muscle tightens

muscle relaxes

forearm up

Straightening your arm

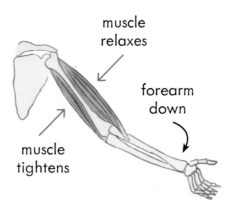

muscle relaxes

forearm down

muscle tightens

Pull your forearm towards your body, then straighten it. Hold your muscles with your other hand. Can you feel them tightening and relaxing?

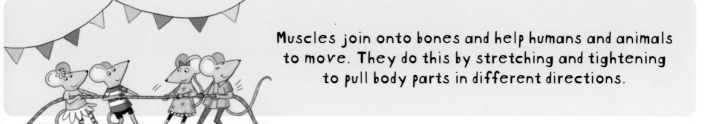

Muscles join onto bones and help humans and animals to move. They do this by stretching and tightening to pull body parts in different directions.

The animals are thinking about why skeletons and muscles are so important. Help them sort their ideas into groups. Draw a line from each idea to the right word to say whether it is about <u>supporting</u>, <u>protecting</u> or <u>moving</u> the body.

SUPPORT	PROTECTION	MOVEMENT

The skull keeps the brain from being damaged.

Muscles in your arm tighten to lift it up.

Without a skeleton, you wouldn't be able to stand up.

Kat

A human's heart is protected by the strong ribcage.

Muscles join onto bones and make them move.

Wolfy

Hop

Pin

Zeb

Draw a line from each speech bubble below to the right word to show whether the answer to each of the animal's clues is 'endoskeleton' or 'exoskeleton'. Look back at pages 20 and 21 to help you.

ENDOSKELETON	EXOSKELETON

Lots of bugs have this kind of skeleton.

Humans have this kind of skeleton.

This skeleton is found outside the body.

This skeleton is found inside the body.

Pin

Gloria

Wolfy

Kat